LAND OF HOPE & STORY

A CELEBRATION OF RURAL BRITAIN'S HISTORY, MYTH AND LEGEND

Told by
Evelyn Foster

Published by Country Books/Ashridge Press
in association with Spiral Publishing Ltd

Country Books Courtyard Cottage, Little Longstone,
Bakewell, Derbyshire DE45 1NN

Tel: 01629 640670
email: dickrichardson@countrybooks.biz

www.countrybooks.biz

in association with Spiral Publishing Ltd
email: jonathan@spiralpublishing.com

ISBN 978-1-910489-85-7

British Library Cataloguing in Publication Data.
A catalogue record for this book is available from the
British Library.

Printed and bound in England by 4edge Limited,
22 Eldon Way Industrial Estate, Hockley, Essex SS5 4AD

Dedication:
For Nigel Sharpe

~ CONTENTS ~

Introduction 9

Forest Fairytales 11

The Spellbinding Scottish Countryside............................ 13

The Knight and the Fairy Queen
A Seelie Tale from Scotland Retold 14

Flora and Fauna of the Forest.. 17

Legends from the Great Welsh Countryside................... 21

Pwyll and the Forest Fair
A Retold Tale from Carmarthenshire...................................... 23

Felix and the Pharisee
A Fairytale from Rural Sussex... 27

British Primroses... 31

The Magic of the Oak Tree.. 32

The Fox and the Oak Tree
A Story told in Hampshire, Lancashire and many British
Shires... 34

Fairy Queens of History and Legend 38

The Poet and the Elf Queen
A Retold Tale from the Scottish Countryside 39

Water Magic in the Countryside.. 43

~ CONTENTS ~

Brett and the Green-Eyed Well Nymph
A Story from Rural Shropshire 48

The Fairy Well
A Fairytale told in Northern Ireland 52

Rhys and the Spirit of the Streams
A Fairytale from Pembrokeshire and many Welsh Shires 54

The Magic of Marsh and Moor 58

The Boy Child and the Elf Child
A Story told in Yorkshire and Perthshire 59

Magic Protection in the Old British landscape 63

The Marsh and the Moon
Fairytale from Lincolnshire 64

The British Countryside and the World 67

Magical Milk in the Countryside 68

The Cobbler and the Elf Man
A Tale from the Derbyshire Countryside 65

Goldilocks and the British Countryside 73

Silverhair and the Three Bears
A Fairytale from Rural Hertfordshire 74

Conclusion 77

~ INTRODUCTION ~

Britain has some of the greatest myths and legends, and many are set in the countryside. In an age when people were close to the land, nature itself was thought 'bewitched!'

Bushes were said to be guarded by cheeky imps like Churn-milk Peg and Melch Dick, trees by grumpy sprites like the Oakmen, and flowers by tiny flower fairies known as pillywiggins.

Our ancestors found fairytales inspiring and uplifting.

History, literature, legend and myth were intertwined in past times.

King Henry II described the bower he built for his beloved, Rosamund, as a ' fairy house,' and James I urged his subjects to make sure their lands were free of fairies. Meanwhile, St Michael's church on Glastonbury Tor (now owned by the National

Trust) was thought to hide an entrance to Fairyland!

Almost anywhere in the British countryside could be the door to another world for our ancestors. Streams, trees, woods and marshes – all have starring roles in British folklore. The most magical ancient landscape of all, though, has always been the forest …

~ FOREST FAIRYTALES ~

The majority of old British stories and fairytales take place in woods and forests. Forests in myth and legend act as bridges between earth and other lands. They are places of transformation where anything can (and often does!) happen.

Forests were well-known and well-loved by our ancestors. Many Old English surnames, like *Foster* and *Forester*, mean 'those who look after the forest.'

Forests were also, historically, places of great danger. King William Rufus was famously killed in the New Forest – shot with an arrow by an unknown assassin. The mystery that surrounds this death has the atmosphere of a fairytale. Ancient forests were also home to wild boar: the emblem of Richard III.

The main forest fairies were thought to be the dryads and the tree elves. The elder tree was said

to be home to a spirit called the Elder Mother.
Belief in her was so strong, people used to ask her
permission before picking elderberries!

It was claimed if you touched twigs from the
elder tree, you could see magical creatures. If you
sat beneath a hawthorn tree, on the other hand, you
might actually meet a fairy. You had to be careful
not to do this on May day, or you could be carried
off to fairyland! Woods and forests were positive
places to our ancestors too. They were seen as
symbols of the journey throughout life itself. They
were also thought places of magic encounters as
this following fairytale shows …

~ THE SPELLBINDING ~
~ SCOTTISH COUNTRYSIDE ~

The Scottish countryside has many great fairytales and many great fairy (Seelie) Queens. The Seelie folk liked to ride out on fairy rades (processions) on wonderful white horses. In rural Scotland, it was traditional to build a cottage with the front and back doors opposite … to allow the fairies to pass through!

This first story takes place on the eve of Samhain, or Halloween, which used to be a magical time in the countryside. It was believed that the barriers between worlds were removed then and spirits could roam abroad.

Folk would light Hallow fires for protection against bad fairies. It was traditional for youths to leap through the flames or run swiftly through the embers. Not all spirits who appeared at this time were hostile. But it paid you to be cautious!

THE KNIGHT AND
~ THE FAIRY QUEEN ~

A SEELIE TALE FROM
SCOTLAND RETOLD

nce a knight got on the wrong side of a decidedly wicked witch. Although the witch loved him, he could not return her love, and this was to prove his undoing.

Although the knight was kind in his rejection, the witch was furious. She took him to the heart of the forest. There she turned him into a snake: a loathsome and terrible beast. Long the snake hid in the forest, lonely and ashamed. Until something unexpected came to pass …

It was the evening before Samhain: that enchanted time between dusk and dawn, between the dawn and the waking. As the moon rose, the snake heard the lilt of a harp, the jingle of harness

14

and the sound of silver bells.

Moments later, strange riders on horses appeared.
A fairy rade of princes, princesses and courtiers. At
their head, rode a woman fair as a flower with eyes
as clear as the day. She was mounted on a white
horse shod in gold. It was the Queen of the Seelies:
the good fairies of Scotland.

The Fairy Queen dismounted and knelt by a tree.
She took the poor snake into her lap and, gently, she
stroked his scales.

Then, softly and sweetly, she sang a magic
song. Clouds paused in their passing and animals
stopped to listen. Forest streams ceased to flow and
sleeping hills shivered. The moon sparkled, the stars
shimmered and the whole world held its breath.

Then, as the song ended, the scales slid away, and
the knight emerged from the snake's skin, whole and
human again.

He started to try and thank the bewitching Fairy
Queen. But, even as the words died on his lips, she
vanished into mist.

~ FLORA AND FAUNA ~ OF THE FOREST

airy forests in stories contained the chief fairy trees: oak, ash and thorn. Branches overhung the path, and if you looked closely, it was said, you could see eyes shining from the leaves. In the National Trust's Hollybush Wood in Sussex, for instance, there are many trees that seemed 'enchanted'.

A tree, like the willow, was said to get bored in the night and walk about muttering to itself! This tradition is probably where Tolkien got his idea for the Ents in *The Lord of the Rings*.

Nobody, of course, loved the British Shires quite as much as J.R.R. Tolkien. It is notable that when the hobbits long to return to their home, a place of peace and beauty, that homeland is known as The Shire.

The countryside is also, of course, a place of many flowers. Flowers in Britain have long been thought to bring about good fortune. The rose, in particular, has always been the symbol of England. The number of pubs called *The Rose and Crown* show its long associations with monarchy.

The historic houses of York and Lancaster had white and red roses as their sigils. The civil war between them famously became known as The Wars Of the Roses. When the victor Henry VII's first son, Arthur, was born, he was known as: 'the rosebush of England'. This was because as the firstborn of Henry of Lancaster and Elizabeth of York, he embodied both red and white roses.

The name Plantagenet, on the other hand means 'broom'. This derived from the yellow broom flower, the 'planta genista', that Geoffrey of Anjou (father of Henry II) used to wear in his helmet.

Katherine of Aragon in British history, and Queen Guinevere in British legend, would ride out on 1st May to collect flowers. This was thought to bring good luck. In 1620, when the Pilgrim Fathers sailed from England for America, they named their ship *The Mayflower*.

Flowers in the olden days were often perceived as magical: especially flowers in forests. Bluebells, for example, summoned fairies to the dance and a foxglove nodding was meant to be a clue that fairy folk were passing. Even better, the presence of cowslips or primroses hinted fairy gold lay nearby. It was best to be wary, though, as fairy gold was not always what it seemed!

Inside flowers, it was said, lay scented rooms and silken-covered walkways. This is where the flower spirits lived. They made their homes inside the bell of the flower and slept on beds of petals.

Magic animals were also believed to live in woodlands. If you saw a white fawn or a golden deer, you knew you'd met a guide to the mysterious Otherworld! Deer have long been revered in both history and folklore. Richard II had a white hart as his sigil, and the first Arthurian adventure was presaged by the arrival of a stag.

LEGENDS FROM
~ THE GREAT WELSH ~
COUNTRYSIDE

The Welsh tradition has many romantic tales and many of these are set in forests. Welsh fairies have a Medieval appearance and are very fond of horses.

Fairies in their stories nearly always appear mounted on a snowy white horse. In fact, horses were very popular in British myth and legend. A symbol of speed and courage, the horse was also the emblem of the doughty Saxon Kings.

The Welsh have more stories than most of human / fairy marriages. These marriages used to be viewed as unions of different 'classes.' The Welsh, of course, had a history of interesting mixed-class marriages. Dowager Queen Katherine, for instance, widow of Henry V, married the Welshman,

Owen Tudor. He was first King Henry V's page, and later, Katherine's groom. They were devoted to one another and one of their descendants was that canny ruler: Henry VII.

~ PWYLL AND THE ~
FOREST FAIR

A RETOLD TALE FROM CARMARTHENSHIRE

In Wales, long ago, there stood an Enchanted Forest. At the edge of this Enchanted Forest, there lay a circle of mounds. It was said, if you stood on one of these mounds, magical things might happen.

Few people dared to go anywhere near the mounds. Fewer still dared to stand on one. Most preferred to stay at home with the blankets up round their ears!

But, Pwyll, Prince of Wales, was braver than most and had always loved adventure. One day, he decided to stand on a mound and take what adventure might come to him.

So, one day, when the sun was high in the sky,

Pwyll stood on a magical mound. Trees hung over the path making a roof above his head. Yet there was no sound. Nothing but the wind in the trees, until …

First, there was a shadow, then a note of music and a mysterious deer appeared. It had a coat of glistening gold and eyes of forest green.

For a moment, the deer looked at Pwyll. Then it vanished.

The next day, Pwyll returned to the mound, and the deer appeared again. Once again, it looked at Pwyll and, once more, disappeared.

On the second and third day, it all happened as before. But, on the third, Pwyll called out:

"Good deer, please stay and talk with me!"

At this, the mysterious deer turned. It shivered, then turned into a woman: A woman with golden hair and eyes of forest green.

"I would you had spoken before," she said; "it needed but a word to stop me."

"I wish I'd known that before! Who are you?" stammered Pwyll.

"I am Rhiannon," the woman told him: "And I seek you, Prince Pwyll, for love."

Speechless, Pwyll gazed at her. Adventure had indeed come upon him. Rhiannon was a woman of fairy, and her name meant 'Great Queen'.

"Return for me in a year," said Rhiannon; "I shall expect you."

Pwyll did as she asked. In a year, he returned to the mound. Rhiannon was waiting for him on a gleaming white horse.

"Follow me," she told him, and again, Pwyll did as she bade him.

He followed the fairy woman through the trees. He followed her past blossom, white like ice, till they reached the deepest part of the forest. There he saw a palace of shimmering stone rising from a lake. A flock of scarlet birds flew around it. Inside there were rooms of satin and lace and many fairy folk dancing.

The fairy folk crowned Pwyll and Rhiannon with flowers and held a feast for them.

They ate and drank with dryads and laughed and joked with tree elves; and water fairies appeared in the pool and sang a song of their adventure.

And, that night, Pwyll and Rhiannon were married.

She became a Princess of Wales and he became a King of the Fair Folk.

And all because Pwyll had gone out one day and stood on a Magical Mound!

~ FELIX AND THE PHARISEE ~

A FAIRYTALE FROM RURAL SUSSEX

nce a young man called Felix caught a pharisee (a fairy). Felix knew how it worked. Many pharisees, he knew, had their own treasure. If you caught one, he had to tell you where it is.

"Where can I find gold?" he asked the pharisee.

"In the golden glade in yonder wood," the pharisee told him.

"The whole glade there is made of gold. It is marked by a tree with a green ribbon."

Felix liked the sound of this! He thought of all the things he could buy with the gold: fine clothes, carriages, a big house.

Everyone would admire him. Rejoicing at the thought of his good fortune, he let the pharisee go.

Felix went into the wood in search of the gold. Yet he felt a bit uneasy. Would the pharisee try to stop him? He knew they could be tricky.

Felix searched the paths for the golden glade. Suddenly, he gasped. He had heard a noise in the bushes. Was it the pharisee?

No! It was only a squirrel. Felix breathed a sigh of relief. He searched for the golden glade. Yet he could not find it.

Imps watched him from the
bushes, yet he did not see them.

Suddenly, Felix thought he
could see something in the branches. Was it the
pharisee? No! It was only a bird.

Felix went on. He looked all through the wood.
But still he could not find the treasure. Silently, the
pillywiggins watched him from the flowers.

"I must be looking in the wrong place!" sighed
Felix. He looked at the glowing trees which had
leaves like emeralds. He looked at the shining plants
which had dew drops like diamonds. But he still
could not see any gold. He was starting to lose hope
now. Would he ever find it.

Suddenly a winter storm blew up! Winds
howled like demons, lightning danced and
dazzled; snowflakes turned into birds of prey and
plunged and pecked at Felix. The mischievous
imps of the bushes joined in and pelted him with
berries.

Then, dimly through the snow, Felix saw a
glimmer. Was it a glimmer of gold? Felix licked his
lips and staggered towards it.

He saw a tree with a green ribbon on it, and his pulse pounded with hope.

Suddenly, the snow vanished. The air felt warm. All the tiredness seemed to melt out of Felix.

"This must be the golden glade!" he thought.

Then he stared.

The glade was rich with primroses. They made a golden carpet on the ground. Pillywiggins peeped at him from the petals. They were grinning all over their tiny faces.

Felix stared again, then his shoulders slumped. Suddenly, he understood.

There never had been any gold, except for the primroses. He had not phrased his question quite right, and the wily pharisee had tricked him.

Felix dug and dug just in case, but he never found any gold.

He had to make do with his comfy old clothes, his comfy old cottage and with travelling about on foot.

In time, he stopped being angry and could laugh about his experience. All the same, from that day on, he kept well away from clever fairies!

~ BRITISH PRIMROSES ~

The star of this story is the British primrose. It was a flower much loved in rural areas as its colour is reminiscent of butter … as well as gold! The primrose was the favourite flower of the Victorian prime minister, Disraeli.

Queen Victoria sent him primroses as tokens of her esteem throughout her reign. At his funeral, she sent a primrose wreath.

THE MAGIC OF
~ THE OAK TREE ~

Forest trees have always been places where fairies were thought to dwell. Acorn Bank Forest in Cumbria, for example, has a mysterious hollow tree: a perfect home for tree elves!

Trees often act as guardians in English stories: both to animals and humans. There is a rich seam of animals, elves and goblins in English folktales... plus a host of spellbinding trees.

The hero of this next story is a tree who acts as forest guardian. It is an oak tree – perhaps the most loved of all the English trees. One of the reasons for its high reputation is that it hid Charles II while he hid from his pursuers.

May 29th, when Charles re-entered London in triumph, is Oak Apple Day in Britain. It was Charles who established many hospitals for veterans in London and in some of the Shires.

In Warwickshire, Oak Apple day is celebrated by decorating the rooms of Leycester hospital for soldiers. In Worcestershire, a Civil War battle site, the Guild Hall gates are hung with oak boughs. Another popular pub name in England is, of course, The Royal Oak!

~ THE FOX AND ~ THE OAK TREE ~

A STORY TOLD IN HAMPSHIRE, LANCASHIRE AND MANY BRITISH SHIRES

There was once a little Fox who lived deep in the forest. One day, Fox was in the heart of the forest when he heard something: A strange kind of panting sound.

Seconds later, Fox found himself staring into the face of … a huge wild boar! The boar looked at him: tongue lolling in a wild grin. Then, slowly, very slowly, it padded towards him.

It opened its jaws and bared its teeth. Then it snarled. It was clear it felt it owned this part of the forest, and woe betide any trespassers.

"Run for your life!" Fox cried to himself and run he certainly did. He ran faster than he had ever

34

run before, chased by the angry wild boar.

Fox ran like a mad thing: Tearing down tracks, throwing himself around corners. He ran with all his might, but the boar was close behind him. Fox's lungs were bursting, his fur was wet with sweat. Yet he tried to keep running as fast as he could, for the huge boar was after him. It chased him over some mud and over a boggy brook.

Fox raced down a forest path. After what seemed like an age, he reached the end of it.

His legs ached. The breath burned in his throat. Fox was tired now. His legs were growing weak. He was, after all, only a small fox. He knew he could not last much longer.

Then, in front of him, Fox saw a Holly Tree.

"Help me," Fox begged the Tree; "before the boar catches me!"

"Me? I don't help just anyone," said the Holly Tree. It was always a prickly kind of tree. So poor Fox had to run on.

The boar was closer still.

Fox ran further into the forest. In front of him was an Elder Tree.

"Help me," Fox begged the Elder Tree;

" before the boar catches me!"

"Me? I'm too old," said the Elder Tree. It was always a rather weary tree.

"I'm too tired to help anyone."

So, with the last of his strength, poor Fox had to run on. His vision was blurred, his legs growing faint. The boar was closer than ever. It seemed hopeless.

Fox limped further into the forest. In front of him was an Oak Tree.

"Help me," the Fox begged the Oak Tree;

"before the boar catches me!"

The Oak Tree looked at him in silence. Fox felt his heart sink.

The boar was almost upon him now.

Then the Oak Tree opened its huge trunk.

"Come in, little Fox," it said, kindly.

"I am the Guardian of the forest. You will be safe here with me."

Fox ran inside. The Oak Tree closed its trunk and hid Fox until the boar had gone.

From that day, Fox made his home with the Oak Tree. He told the Tree what went on outside the forest, and the Oak Tree kept on keeping him safe from boars.

So everyone was happy. But the wild boar never did find out what had happened to the fast little Fox!

FAIRY QUEENS OF
~ HISTORY AND LEGEND ~

he following
Great British
story features
an elven Queen.
Royalty itself once
seemed mystical to our
ancestors. Elizabeth I,
for example, was
widely known, thanks
to the poet Spenser, as
'The Faerie Queene'.

THE POET AND THE ELF QUEEN

A RETOLD TALE FROM THE SCOTTISH COUNTRYSIDE

Once, long ago, there lived a poet known as Thomas the Rhymer. Thomas could sing and play as well as the elves and his words were beyond compare.

One day, Thomas was playing his lute in the nearby forest, when, who should appear before him, but a commanding Elven Queen. She wore a mantle of green gossamer and in her hair a silver star gleamed.

The Queen was enchanted by Thomas' playing. She took him by the hand and led him further into the forest. Every step was on flowers, soft beneath their feet, as if they trod together on clouds.

Their journey took them through a realm of

night where blood swirled round Thomas' knees. Their journey took them across a coal-black heath and over a midnight meadow.

Then the Queen showed Thomas an easier path: the path of perdition. She showed him a hard and narrow path: the path of righteousness.

"Yet for poets, singers and lovers of beauty there is a third way," she told him.

Then she led him to a magic path, rich with moss, and so she brought him to fairyland!

The land shone in a light bright like the sun, yet mild like the moon. It was filled with a wild scent that stroked the nostrils.

There were rivers clearer than any on earth and waterfalls with droplets like pearls.

Thomas lived with the Queen in Fairyland for many a happy year. Then, when the Queen judged the time to be right, he returned to his mortal home.

And when Thomas returned to the human world, his songs, his music and his poems were even lovelier than before. For he was now inspired in all he did by the magic of the Elven Queen.

More years passed in the mortal world, till

Thomas reached old age. Then, one morning, a milk-white fawn came to the place where he lived. None of the villagers knew what its coming meant. But, Thomas knew.

Smiling, Thomas said farewell to his friends, and followed the fawn into the forest.

No mortal soul ever saw Thomas the Rhymer again. But it is said, like all poets and lovers of beauty, he dwells with the powerful Elven Queen, and lives in Fairyland!

WATER MAGIC IN THE COUNTRYSIDE

ater is especially bewitching in old and well-loved tales. Since water is a necessity of life, to our ancestors it seemed a spiritual thing.

In Ancient Britain, it was believed to be a link between this realm and the next. Any water source could be a link with Fairyland, and water was thought to symbolize the truth beneath the surface. Each well, river and stream was believed to have its own goddess or water fairy.

The old British Shire custom of well dressing (decorating wells with flowers, greenery and ribbons) was intended both to appease these spirits and ensure a supply of clean water.

The most famous water fairy in British folklore is, of course, the Lady of the Lake. She brings up

Lancelot in her underwater realm and teaches him
knightly skills. She also gives King Arthur his famous
sword – returned to her on his death. Most British
monarchs were at some time in love with Arthurian
legends. Athelstan was believed to have inspired the
character of Lancelot, Richard I gave away a sword
he claimed was Excalibur, while Edward III had a
round table made and clothes embroidered with the
story of Tristan and Isolde.

Henry VII named his eldest son, Arthur, to
associate his house with the myth. He meant to
imply that the reign of the Tudors would bring
chivalry and prosperity to England.

Growing up, Prince Arthur and his young brother,
the future Henry VIII, were both fans of Arthurian
legend. When he was King, Henry liked to think of
his kingdom as Camelot, while Thomas of Lancaster
liked to think that he was living in Avalon!

Indeed the Arthurian stories are well-known and
loved throughout the whole of Britain. Most of them
hail from Nottinghamshire, Wales and the West
Country: especially Cornwall. However, there are
other lesser- known stories too, set in and around water.

SHE·SPENT·THE·WHOLE·DAY·NEAR·THE·FOUNTAIN

There are both male and female water fairies in British folklore. Female fairies often have long green hair, while male fairies are more likely to have long green teeth! Baby water fairies are sometimes called urchins. This word came to mean a naughty child, which shows the mischievous nature of fairies.

This next tale is set at harvest time: another vital date in the countryside. Before the mechanization of farms, the harvest was a great occasion. It was brought home in triumph, in wains covered in flowers, with workers singing and blowing horns. That night, the harvest home feast would be held. This involved roast beef, plum puddings, apple pies … and rather a lot of cider!

A Sussex harvest song has the words:

I have drunk nine, and I will drink ten;
Now I think it's my turn to drink again!

While a traditional harvest song, sung in both Berkshire and Oxfordshire, goes as follows:

Here's a health unto our master,
The founder of our feast;
We hope his soul to God will go
When he do get his rest.
So drink, boys, drink,
And see you do not spill,
For if you do, you shall drink two …
For that be the master's will!

Cider was also used to wassail the orchards: especially in rural Sussex. Wassail comes from the Anglo Saxon *was hal* (good health). Cider was poured round the roots of apple trees to ensure a healthy crop for the year.

In the following tale from Shropshire, however, the workers (unusually!) crave water not cider. This, as you will see, has unexpected consequences …

BRETT AND THE
~ GREEN-EYED WELL NYMPH ~

A STORY FROM RURAL SHROPSHIRE

Long ago in Shropshire, there lived a young man called Brett. One day, Brett was bringing in the harvest with his father and his brothers. The sun blazed down on the golden crops and the heads of the harvesters. Soon they were wiping their faces and complaining their throats felt parched.

"Fetch us a drink, Brett, there's a good lad," cried his father;

"we're perishing in this heat. I can't wait for my cider at harvest home. I need a drink right now!"

Good-naturedly, Brett took a water jug and went to the well several fields away. Brett had always been fascinated by this well. Enchantment seemed to linger around it.

Before he filled the water jug, Brett sat on the edge of the well. The atmosphere was strangely cooler here and time itself seemed suspended.

Then, suddenly, Brett tensed all over: he had seen something. A shadow had moved on the water. Carefully, he moved towards it. He hoped he was not going to encounter the unpredictable nature imp, Puck.

Rising up from the well, he found, not Puck, but a water nymph with heavy dark hair. Brett stared into her leaf-green eyes and at once fell under her spell.

"I would beg a kiss, with your permission," he stammered.

Then the water nymph smiled at him.

"It shall be yours," she promised.

The young man's face filled with desire and he bent over the well and kissed her. The nymph rose from the well and melted into his arms. Her breath fluttered against his own like the touch of fairy wings.

Brett traced every feature of her face with his fingers as though it were precious to him. The

nymph's arms came up and held him. Then she carried him down to her underwater world where only the water fairies reign.

The family of Brett looked for him, long and hard, among both field and fountain. But, however long and hard they looked, they never saw him again!

You clearly had to be careful around wells in stories as this tale from Northern Ireland also shows. In Irish folklore, a fairy is known as a sidhe (pronounced shee).

~ THE FAIRY WELL ~

A FAIRYTALE TOLD IN NORTHERN IRELAND

One dark night, a young girl called Maeve was collecting water from the well. There was just enough light from the stars to see by. Maeve reached over the well, and to her terror, something pulled her in!

Down, down, down she fell, till she landed on soft damp earth. Next moment, there was someone standing over her – a man in red with pointed ears. She knew at once that this was a Prince of the Sidhe!

"Come, dance with me!" the Prince said, and seconds later, they were standing in the ballroom of a palace. It had golden tables spread with food and walls covered with silk.

So the Human and the Sidhe danced together:

Leaping and spinning round the ballroom. The Sidhe whirled Maeve till they were both dizzy and gasping for breath. They stopped and the Sidhe indicated the golden tables heaped with food.

"Will you eat with me?" he asked Maeve with a courtly bow.

A tiny voice whispered in Maeve's ear.

"Do not eat, or you will never get back to your Mother!"

"No thank you, sir", she answered him.

"I truly have to go home."

At that, there was a buzzing like an angry swarm of bees, and all the lights went out. Maeve found herself standing back by the well, her pitcher in her hand.

Maeve ran at top speed home to her Mother.

But, after that, she never went to fetch water after dark again!

~ RHYS AND THE SPIRIT ~ OF THE STREAMS

A FAIRYTALE FROM PEMBROKESHIRE AND MANY WELSH SHIRES

In Wales, there were fields that looked like velvet: watered by ribbons of streams. These streams were thought to be magical. A water spirit was said to inhabit them.

A young man called Rhys had always loved this story. So, one day, he decided to enter the fields and find the Spirit of the Streams.

Rhys went into the fields. He walked for a while without seeing anything unusual. At last, he stopped, gasping for breath. He was extremely thirsty.

All of a sudden, his eyes lit up. He had spied one of the streams. Heart thumping, Rhys bent to drink from it.

Then, he gasped. There sat the Spirit in a golden

boat combing her golden hair! Rhys immediately fell in love with her. Yet at the sight of him, the Spirit dived into the stream and disappeared.

From that day, Rhys could not eat. He could not sleep. He could only think about the Spirit. At last, after days in which he could not even eat his breakfast, Rhys knew he had to do something. So he went to see the Witch of the Woodlands in her house within a circle of stones.

The Witch's house was tall and dark and grim. Tallness, darkness and grimness seemed to seep from the very stones. A flight of steps led up to it. Rhys climbed the steps. Rhys reached the top of the steps and the Witch opened the door.

"Come in!" cried the Witch.

Knees knocking, Rhys came in.

Once in, he felt better. The Witch turned out to be a Good Witch.

"What can I do for you?" she asked him.

"I have fallen in love with the Spirit of the Stream, and I don't know what to do!" Rhys cried.

Then the Witch smiled.

"Take bread and cheese and throw it into the

stream," she told him; "then you may gain your heart's desire."

Rhys thanked her, fervently. He returned to the forest and dropped bread and cheese into the stream. He did this a second and then a third time.

There was silence. Nothing happened. Rhys bit his lip. Had the advice been wrong after all?

Then, suddenly, there was a ripple. A fountain rose up from the stream. Then as Rhys held his breath, a Spirit appeared in the fountain!

" Lady," cried Rhys with all his heart;

"will you consent to marry me?"

Without speaking, the Spirit inclined her graceful head. Then she reached out and pulled him under the water. That was the last that was known of him. It is said that Rhys lives there still as a monarch among the water nymphs.

~ THE MAGIC OF
~ MARSH AND MOOR ~

Marshes too seemed magical to the Ancient Britons. A potent mixture of earth and water, they were thought to be haunted by evil spirits and dark fairies. You had to watch your words among marsh fairies too, as this next tale makes only too clear!

THE BOY CHILD
AND THE ELF CHILD

A STORY TOLD IN YORKSHIRE AND PERTHSHIRE

 n a small house, there once lived a widow and her small boy. The boy's name was Boyd. Boyd and his Mother lived near a marsh which was believed to be magic.

The marsh had hollows where boggarts and elves were thought to live, and where mysterious lights danced at night. It was said that sometimes the elves from the marsh would visit the world of humans.

One night, Boyd would not go to bed. So his Mother went up without him. Boyd sat alone by the fire. Then he heard noises.

Scary noises, hairy noises, as if someone was on the roof!

Boyd had a feeling that something was seriously

wrong. Then he heard more noises: as if someone was about to climb down the chimney.

Slowly, very slowly, Boyd crept across his floor. Slowly, very slowly, Boyd crept to his door. Then he almost yelled aloud.

Something was on his face!

Seconds later, Boyd relaxed. It was just his shirt hanging on the door. He had completely forgotten it was there. Boyd opened his bedroom door and stepped into the hall.

It was black in the hall. Thrilling black. Chilling black. Boyd crept along by the wall. Then he froze. Something was in the hall.

Boyd's heart rate went back down as he saw what it was. It was just his old wooden toy chest.

Breathing hard, Boyd got to the top of the stairs. CRR-ACK!

CRR-ACK! went first one stair then the other under Boyd's nervous feet. Boyd reached the bottom of the stairs and opened the sitting room door.

Then he gasped. Someone had indeed come down the chimney: the tiniest girl you ever saw. She had tiny hands, tiny feet and bright scarlet hair. She was an elf child from the magic marsh!

"Can I play with you, human boy?" the elf girl cried.

"I've come especially from the marsh of the elves and boggarts to meet a human child."

Boyd's breathing went back to normal. It was all right. She only wanted to play.

"What is your name, elf girl?" he asked her.

"My Own Self," the elf child replied.

"What is your name, human boy?"

"My Own Self too," said Boyd, cautiously. He was not sure he wanted to tell the elf his true name.

So the boy child and the elf child played together. The elf child made animals out of ash. They came to life and played with the children. She made tiny houses with tiny men and women which also came to life and played with them. They all had great fun, till a spark from the fire burnt the elf child's tiny foot.

Then she screamed and the magic figures vanished.

A great big voice roared out: "WHAT HAS HAPPENED?"

"My foot got burnt!" the elf child cried.

"WHO DID THIS TO YOU?" roared the voice.

"My Own Self," the elf child replied.

"Well, if you did it yourself, it's your own stupid fault!" said the voice, rather grumpily. It was a boggart: a goblin guardian of the child! A long hairy arm reached down the chimney and pulled the elf child away.

Boyd ran fast up the stairs. He ran fast down the hall. He jumped fast into his bed and pulled the pillows fast round his head.

The marsh folk never came back. Yet, after that, Boyd went to bed when he was told.

After all... you never knew!

~ MAGIC PROTECTION IN THE ~
OLD BRITISH LANDSCAPE

The next story shows the old custom of carrying hazel and rowan. Twigs from trees, like the rowan and the hazel, were thought to be protection against bad fairies. In Aberdeenshire, it was customary to make crosses out of rowan twigs. These were then placed over doors and windows to ward off evil spirits and wicked witches!

King James the Sixth of Scotland and the First of England certainly believed in witches. He wrote a book called Daemonologie: a detailed study of demons, spirits and witches. It is widely believed this book influenced Shakespeare's 'Macbeth'.

James was always seeking ways to defeat evil forces, and would probably have liked this next story...

~ THE MARSH AND ~
THE MOON

A FAIRYTALE FROM LINCOLNSHIRE

In the time, when the world was wild, there was a magic marsh in Lincolnshire. The marsh had deep dark bogs where few had dared to tread. And these deep dark bogs, it was said, were haunted by even darker spirits!

High in the sky, the Moon felt sad to see such a terrible place. So, one day, the Moon came down from the sky to see if she could help.

As she touched the earth, the Moon shivered. Then she turned into a woman: a woman with long white hair and eyes of shining silver.

Suddenly, she gasped. A man was walking across the dark marsh. He was about to fall into a bog and be caught by the evil spirits.

The Moon shone with all her might. By her rays,

the man saw the bog just in time and avoided it. He ran away at top speed.

But the evil spirits, the witches and bogles of the bog, were angry that the Moon had warned the man. They rushed at the kindly Moon and seized her. Then, cackling and gloating, they buried her in a coffin deep within the marsh.

Now the Moon was gone from the sky and the whole world went dark. People bumped into houses, walls and each other! They fell into puddles and pools. It was chaos.

The man the Moon had saved felt terrible. He knew what had happened was all on his account. He gathered together his neighbours and friends. They went out on the marsh to try and find the Moon.

They held hazel and rowan twigs in their hands to keep the evil ones at bay. Then they dug until they found the coffin.

They brought it up and opened it. The kindly Moon soared out and flew back to the sky, and the evil spirits were confounded.

From that day, the Moon lights the sky every night …. for all her friends on earth who once helped her!

THE BRITISH COUNTRYSIDE AND THE WORLD

There are also fairytales in the British countryside which are versions of stories from other lands. The following tale about a cobbler, for instance, is the Derbyshire version of the German tale: The Elves and the Shoemaker.

~ MAGICAL MILK IN ~
~ THE COUNTRYSIDE ~

his story also includes the custom, once popular in rural Britain, of leaving milk out for the fairies.

In the Scottish Shires, pouring milk for the fairies was known as 'milk to the hairy ones!'

Many households would do this as a matter of course before turning in for the night.

Yorkshire fairies were also wild for mortal milk.

Allegedly, it gave them greater strength. It was even believed that some fairies liked to suckle at a new mother's breast: in order to get as much milk as possible!

Many fairies were believed to help with household tasks. In Sussex folklore, there is a fairy known as Dobbs who would help around the house, if needed.

Dobbs was easily offended, though, as were most house fairies. This tale from Derbyshire is a good example, though this fairy is called Hobb, not Dobbs.

THE COBBLER AND
~ THE ELF MAN ~

A TALE FROM THE DERBYSHIRE COUNTRYSIDE

nce there was a cobbler whose name was Jim. He was so poor, even the rats felt sorry for him!

Soon he could not even afford leather to make new shoes.

"I'm finished," Jim thought to himself.

Sadly, Jim went to bed. Yet, sad as he was, poor as he was, he did not forget to leave milk out for the fairies. It was said an elf called Hob lived nearby who was very fond of milk.

The next day, Jim woke up. He looked. He gasped.

The milk was gone. In its place was a pair of new shoes!

"I bet they were made by Hob," thought Jim. He looked again.

But he could not see anyone.

"Thank you, Hob!" he called out. But there was no reply.

Jim sold the shoes. He made enough money for more leather.

He made enough money for more food.

That night, he left out both milk and bread. It was said Hob was very fond of bread.

The next day, Jim woke up. He looked. He gasped.

The milk was gone. The bread was gone. In their place were three pairs of new shoes.

"I could get to like this!" thought Jim. He looked. But he still could not see anyone.

"Thank you again, Hob," he called. But there was still no reply.

Jim sold the shoes. He made even more money.

That night, he left out milk, bread and a cake. It was said Hob was very fond of cake.

The next day, Jim woke up. He gasped harder than ever.

There were shoes everywhere. There were shoes on the tables, shoes on the chairs, and shoes bursting out of all the drawers!

There were shoes in all the buckets and shoes in all the basins. What was he going to do?

Jim could only breathe by throwing half the shoes out of the window.

"Hob, Hob, please stop!" he called. Hob heard him. Offended, Hob stopped.

After that, Hob no longer made shoes for Jim. But he no longer needed to. Thanks to him, Jim now had so many shoes to sell, he was wealthy all his life.

But he still left milk out to be on the safe side.

And at least the cats enjoyed it!

~ GOLDILOCKS AND THE ~ BRITISH COUNTRYSIDE

oldilocks and the Three Bears was once thought to be an original work by the poet, Robert Southey. But it is now believed he borrowed it from tales from the Old English countryside.

It is interesting that the original Goldilocks was an old woman, not a child, and in the Yorkshire version, a fox! Here is one of the several versions that hail from Hertfordshire.

Incidentally, SilverHair, as she is called in the rural tale, is a better rhyme for 'bear' than Goldilocks!

~ SILVERHAIR AND THE ~ THREE BEARS

A FAIRYTALE FROM RURAL HERTFORDSHIRE

ilverHair was an Old Lady. She lived on her own near a small wood and was never polite to her neighbours.

One day, SilverHair felt restless. So she went for a walk in the wood. At first, it was not too bad. The Old Lady felt the exercise doing her good. But, after a while, she felt tired.

She went a little deeper into the wood. There, to her great surprise, she found a strange and mysterious house!

The door was open, so SilverHair went in.

Inside she saw a table and three chairs: one big, one medium, one small. The big chair was too hard for the Old Lady and the medium chair too soft.

But the third smaller chair was just right. So not being very polite, the Old Lady sat on it.

Then she saw three bowls of porridge on the table. She tried the first big bowl, but it was too hot. The second medium-sized bowl was too cold. But the third smaller bowl was just right. So not being even slightly polite, the Old Lady ate it all.

After that, she went upstairs. Here she saw three beds. The first two were too high, but the smallest was just the right height for her. The Old Lady lay down and fell asleep.

But, before long, the family who owned the house came home.

The family were tall and hairy and scary. They were, in fact, three talking Bears!

"Who has sat on my chair?" roared Mr Bear.

"Who has sat on my chair?" roared Mrs Bear.

" Who has sat on my chair?" roared Baby Bear.

Then they saw the three bowls of porridge.

"Who has been eating my porridge?" roared Mr Bear.

"Who has been eating my porridge?" roared Mrs Bear.

"Who has been eating my porridge and eaten it all up?" roared Baby Bear.

They rushed upstairs and found the terrified Old Lady. The family towered over her.

"Shall we beat her?" roared Mr Bear.

"Shall we hang her?" roared Mrs Bear.

"Shall we roast her?" roared Baby Bear.

Before they could decide which they'd like best, SilverHair jumped out of the window, and ran, safe, away.

She never bothered the bears again. But, after that, she was always polite to her neighbours ... so everyone lived happily ever after!

~ CONCLUSION ~

s we have seen, Great British stories
(as well as being great British fun!) have
always had a social function.

They strove to entertain, to inspire each
generation to learn about their past, and give them
hope for a better future. They championed courage,
kindness and care for nature, and showed adversity
can be overcome.

Discourtesy is always punished in fairytales.
Greed is also punished. Characters who crave too
much of anything often come to a sticky end!

As Dickens said: 'It is a matter of grave
importance that fairytales should be respected.'
The folklore scholars, Iona and Peter Opie, agreed,
noting: 'Magic encourages speculation... and a man
without speculation might as well walk on four legs...
a child or adult who does not feel wonder is but an
inlet for apple pie!'

So let's celebrate our great British stories and our great British countryside. If we do, we may finally create a world in which we all live more happily ever after...!

~ OTHER BOOKS BY EVELYN ~

Include:

Frozen Fairytales For All Ages
(Country Books)

The Elves and the Trendy Shoes
(Tadpole Fairytale Twists: Hodder Headline)

The Mermaid of Cafur
(Barefoot Books)

The Bone Giant
(Leapfrog World Tales)

Alan and the Animals
(Hachette)

~ ABOUT THE AUTHOR ~

Evelyn Foster lives in rural Sussex. She has a First in English Literature from London University, and an inter-disciplinary MA in drama, history and legend from York.

She has worked as an author, storyteller and actress, has spoken on fairytales at the Royal Festival Hall and appeared in fantasy art as a dryad. She has read to the blind, done drama with disabled children, and run myth and acting workshops at the British Museum. She has played Shakespearean, Medieval and Victorian heroines ... and a number of Fairy Godmothers and Elven Queens!

Evelyn has also written for magazines such as: Country Lovers, Country Living, Country Origins and Downs Country.